Good News
in
paper

He was my friend,
no,
he was my brother
...Jacques Desnoyers.
Claude

Good News in paper

Claude Lafortune

CANADIAN BIBLE SOCIETY

1835 YONGE STREET, TORONTO, ONTARIO M4S 1Y1

Visual Concept: Claude Lafortune

Text in French edition: Henriette Major

Research for French original concept:
Jean-Guy Dubuc

Photography: Jean-Louis Frund

Photography, pages 23 and 44: Pierre Labelle

Drawing page 46: Nathalie Lafortune,
8 years of age

Director of publication,
French edition: Raymonde Simard-Martin

Director of publication,
English edition: Howard G. Zurbrigg

This book was first published in French under the title
"L'Evangile en papier", by Henriette Major and Claude Lafortune;
published by La Corporation des Editions Fides in 1977. (ISBN 0-7755-0641-9)

ISBN 0-88834-058-3

TEV593P   Printed in Canada   CBS-1978-20M

Mary and Joseph

There was a Jewish girl named Mary who lived in the town of Nazareth. She was engaged to a man named Joseph, who was a descendant of King David.

The Angel Gabriel is Sent to Mary

God sent the Angel Gabriel to her with a message. The angel said to her, "God has sent me with some good news for you! The Lord is with you and will show you great kindness!"

The angel's words troubled Mary. She did not understand what he meant. Then the angel said to her, "Don't be afraid, Mary. God is pleased with you. You will have a son, and you will name him Jesus. He will be a great person. He will be the Son of the Most High God. The Lord God will make him a king, as his ancestor David was. He will be king over his people forever. His kingdom will never end!"

But Mary said to the angel, "I am not married. How can all of this happen?"

The angel answered, "The power of God's Spirit will come down to you, and you will have a baby. This holy child will be called the Son of God. People have said that your cousin Elizabeth could not have any children. But three months from now she will have a baby, even though she is very old. There is nothing that God cannot do."

Then Mary said, "I am God's Servant. I will do whatever you say." And the angel left her.

6

An Angel is Sent to Joseph

Mary and Joseph were engaged, but before they lived together, she told him that she was going to have a baby by the power of God's Spirit.

Joseph was a man who always did what was right. He knew that he was not the father of the baby, but he did not want to put Mary to shame before all the people. So he said to himself, "I will break the engagement in private."

While Joseph was thinking about this, an angel of the Lord came to him in a dream and said, "Joseph, descendant of King David, do not worry. Mary will have a son by God's Spirit. Do not hesitate to marry her. You will name him Jesus, which means Saviour, for he will save his people from their sins."

Now all this happened so that what God had said through the prophet would come true. God had said, "A virgin will have a son, and people will call him Immanuel." In the Hebrew language, Immanuel means "God is with us."

So when Joseph woke up from the dream, he did as God's angel had told him. He married Mary, but they did not sleep together, until the baby was born. When the baby came, Joseph named him Jesus.

Mary Visits Elizabeth

Soon after the angel had spoken to Mary, she got ready and hurried off to visit her cousin Elizabeth. Elizabeth and her husband Zechariah lived in a town in the hill country of Judea. Mary went into the house and greeted Elizabeth, who was also expecting a baby. When Elizabeth heard Mary's greetings, the baby moved in her body. Then God's Spirit spoke through Elizabeth, and she said in a loud voice, "God has chosen you for a special purpose! He has shown greater kindness to you than to any other woman. And he will show great kindness to your son! It is so wonderful that my Lord's mother would come to visit me! As soon as you greeted me, my baby jumped with happiness. You have something to be happy about because God has blessed you! You believe that his promise to you will come true!"

Mary's Song of Praise

"I praise the Lord God my Saviour,
  for he has made me glad.
I was only his servant girl,
  but he was kind to me.
From now on all people will say
  how kind God has been to me.
God, who is mighty and holy,
  has done great things for me.

God is always kind to people who obey him;
  he is merciful to everyone who honours him.
He has used his mighty strength
  to destroy proud men and ruin their plans.
He has taken powerful kings from their thrones
  and given humble men their places.
He fills hungry people with good things to eat,
  and sends the rich away with empty hands.

The Lord has kept the promise he made long ago,
  to come and help his people Israel.
He has shown mercy to the descendants of Abraham,
  as he promised to do forever."

    Mary stayed with Elizabeth for about three months, and then she went back home.

9

The Birth of Jesus

Not long before Jesus was born, Emperor Augustus gave orders for all of the people in the Roman Empire to be counted and their names written down. When this first count was made, Quirinius was the governor of Syria. Everyone had to go back to his own home town so that a count could be made.

So Joseph went from the town of Nazareth in Galilee to the town of Bethlehem in Judea. Bethlehem was the town where King David was born, and Joseph went there to be counted because he was a descendant of David. Mary, who was engaged to Joseph, went with him. She was expecting a baby, but there was no room for her and Joseph to stay in the inn.

While they were there in Bethlehem, the time came for Mary's baby to be born. It was her first child, and he was a boy. She wrapped him in baby clothes and placed him in a manger.

The Shepherds and the Angels

Near the town of Bethlehem there were some shepherds, who were spending the night in the fields, taking care of their sheep. An angel of God came to the shepherds, and the glory of God shone all around. They were terribly afraid, but the angel said to them, "Don't be afraid! I have good news for you, and it will bring great joy to all the people. Today in David's town your Saviour was born. He is Christ the Lord! And here is how you can find him. He is wrapped in baby clothes and lying in a manger.

Suddenly many other angels came and stood beside that angel. Then they all sang praises to God:
"Praise God who lives in heaven above.
He gives peace to all on earth, who do what pleases him."

After that, the angels went back to heaven, and the shepherds said to one another, "Let's go to Bethlehem and see what has happened. Let's see what God has told us about."

So they hurried off to Bethlehem. When they got there, they found Mary and Joseph and saw the baby lying in the manger, just as the angel had said. Then they told Mary and Joseph what the angel had said about the child. Everyone was amazed at what the shepherds said. Mary remembered all these things and thought about them again and again. The shepherds went back, and on their way they sang praises to God for all that they had heard and seen.

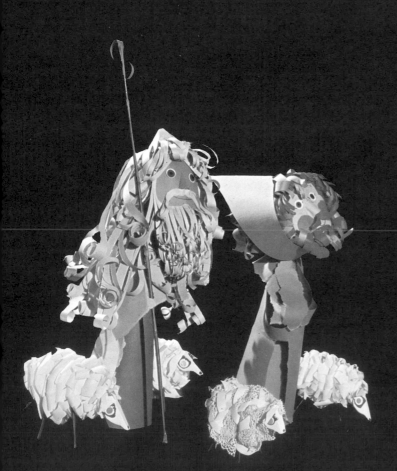

Visitors from the East

Jesus was born in the town of Bethlehem in Judea during the time when Herod was king. Soon afterward, some men who studied the stars came from the east to Jerusalem. They asked, "Where is the baby who was born to be the king of the Jews? We saw his star when it came up in the east, and we have come to worship him."

When King Herod heard about this, he was very upset, and so was everyone else in Jerusalem. He called together all the chief priests and the teachers of the Scriptures, and he asked them, "Where will God's Chosen King be born?"

"In the town of Bethlehem in Judea," they answered. Then they told him what the prophet had written: "People say that you, Bethlehem, are not the most important town in Judea. But a man will come from your town who will lead my people Israel."

So Herod called the visitors from the east to a secret meeting and found out from them the exact time that they had first seen the star. Then he told them, "Go to Bethlehem. Search carefully for the child. And when you find him, let me know, so that I too may go and worship him."

The men left, and on their way they saw the same star that they had seen in the east. How happy they were to see it! How excited they became! The star went on ahead of them until it stopped over the place where the child was. They went into the house, and when they saw the child with his mother Mary, they knelt down and worshipped him. They brought out their gifts of gold, frankincense, and myrrh, and presented them to him.

Then they went back to their own country by another road, since God had warned them in a dream not to go back to Herod.

Jesus in the Temple

Every year Jesus' parents went to the city of Jerusalem for the Passover Festival. When Jesus was twelve years old, the family went to the festival as usual. After the festival was over, Jesus' parents started back home, but Jesus stayed in Jerusalem. His parents did not know this. They thought that he was with some of the other people in the group travelling back to Nazareth. So they travelled all day long and then began to look for him among their relatives and friends, but they did not find him. Then they went back to Jerusalem and started looking for him there. On the third day they found him in the Temple with some of the teachers of the Scriptures. He was sitting there, listening to them and asking them questions. Everyone who heard him was amazed at his wise answers. His parents were surprised to find him there, and his mother asked him, "Son, why have you done this to us? Your father and I have been very worried. We have been looking everywhere for you."

Jesus answered them, "Why did you have to look for me? Didn't you know that I had to be in the Temple, which is my Father's house?" But they did not understand what he meant.

Then Jesus went back to Nazareth with his parents. He lived there with them and obeyed them. But his mother remembered all these things, and she kept thinking about them. Jesus grew up, and as he grew, he became wiser. People liked him, and God was pleased with him.

14

15

16

John the Baptist

The Jews looked for God to send someone to save them and their nation. Sometimes they called this person "the Chosen One" or "the Chosen King". At other times the Jews thought that God would send the prophet Elijah once again or that he would send some other prophet, called "the Great Prophet".

One day the Jewish leaders in Jerusalem sent some priests and some of the priests' helpers to ask John the Baptist who he was. They asked him, "Are you the Chosen One?"

John did not try to hide the truth. He spoke clearly so that they could understand. He said, "I am not the Chosen One."

"Who are you then?" they asked. "Are you Elijah?"

"No, I am not," John answered.

"Are you the Great Prophet?" they asked.

"No," he said.

"Then tell us who you are," they said. "We have to give an answer to the people who sent us. Who do you say you are?"

So John told them what the prophet Isaiah had said, "I am only someone who shouts in the desert. I tell people to make a straight path for the Lord to travel on."

Some of the men who had been sent were those who strictly obeyed the rules of their religion. They asked John, "You say that you are not the Chosen One, or Elijah, or the Great Prophet. Then why do you baptize people?"

John answered, "I baptize people with water. But there is someone here that you do not know. He will come later, and I am not good enough even to untie his sandals."

All this happened near the town of Bethany on the east side of the Jordan River, where John was baptizing.

Jesus of Nazareth

The Baptism of Jesus

While John was baptizing people in the Jordan River, Jesus left Galilee and went there to be baptized by John. But John tried to make Jesus change his mind. He said to him, ''I need to be baptized by you. Why have you come here to be baptized by me?''

Jesus answered, ''This is what God wants us to do now. In this way we will obey God completely.''

As soon as Jesus was baptized, he came up out of the water. Heaven opened, and he saw the Spirit of God come down like a dove upon him. Then a voice from heaven said, ''This is my own dear Son. I am pleased with him.''

The First Followers of Jesus

About four o'clock the next afternoon, John was again standing near the Jordan River with two of his followers. When he saw Jesus walking by, he said, "There is the Lamb of God."

The two followers heard him say this, and they went along behind Jesus. Then Jesus turned around and saw them following him. So he asked them, "What are you looking for?"

They answered him by asking, "Where do you live, Rabbi?" (In the Hebrew language "Rabbi" means "Teacher".)

"Come and see," he told them. So they went with him and saw where he lived. They spent the rest of the day with him.

One of them was Andrew, Simon's brother. At once he found his brother Simon and told him, "We have found the Chosen One, the one we call Christ." Then he took Simon to Jesus.

Jesus looked at him and said, "Your name is Simon, but you will be called Peter." (The word Peter means "a rock".)

Simon Peter

John

James

Andrew

Philip

Bartholomew

Matthew

Thomas

These are the twelve men whom Jesus chose to be his close followers.

James, the son of Alphaeus

Simon

Thaddaeus

Judas Iscariot

The Wedding in Cana

Jesus' mother had been invited to a wedding in the town of Cana in Galilee, and so had Jesus and his followers. When the guests had drunk all the wine, Jesus' mother said to him, "They are out of wine."

"You must not tell me what to do," Jesus answered. "It is not the right time for me to show who I really am."

Jesus' mother then told the servants, "Do whatever he tells you."

The Jewish religion had rules about washing before meals. And so there were six stone water jars there. Each jar was large enough to hold more than twenty gallons. Jesus said to the servants, "Fill these jars with water." The servants filled them to the top, and then Jesus told them, "Now dip out some of the water and take it to the man in charge of the feast." When they took the water to him, it had become wine.

The man did not know where the wine had come from, but the servants knew. He tasted the wine and then called the man who was getting married. He said to him, "Everyone else serves the best wine first. And after the guests have drunk a lot, he serves the wine that is not as good. But you have kept the best wine until now."

It was in Cana of Galilee that Jesus did this first miracle. There he showed what wonderful power he had, and his followers put their trust in him.

The Miraculous Catch of Fish

One day Jesus was standing on the shore of Lake Galilee. People were crowding around him to hear him teach about God. Jesus saw two boats pulled up on the beach. One of the boats belonged to Simon Peter. He and the other fishermen had left them there and were washing their fishing nets. Jesus got into Simon's boat and asked him to push off a little from the shore. Then Jesus sat down in the boat and taught the crowd.

When he finished teaching the people, he said to Simon, "Push the boat out into the deep water. Then you and your partners let down your nets to catch fish."

Simon answered, "Master, we have worked hard all night long and have caught nothing. But if you say so, I will let down the nets." They did it and caught so many fish that the nets were about to break. Then they gave a signal for the men in the other boat to come and help them. They came and filled both boats so full of fish that the boats were about to sink. When Simon saw what had happened, he fell on his knees before Jesus and said, "Go away from me, Lord. I am a sinful man."

Simon and the men with him were amazed at how many fish they had caught. Zebedee's sons, James and John, who were Simon's partners, were also amazed. Jesus said to Simon, "Don't be afraid. From now on you will be catching men." They pulled their boats up on the beach, left everything, and followed Jesus.

Jesus Heals a Crippled Man

Some teachers of the Scriptures and some men who strictly obeyed all the rules of their religion had heard about Jesus and came to listen to him. They came from every town in Galilee and Judea and from the city of Jerusalem. They were sitting and listening to Jesus teach, and God gave him the power to heal sick people.

Some men came, carrying a crippled man on a cot. They tried to take him into the house in order to bring him to Jesus, but they could not get through the crowd. So they carried him up on the roof and made a hole there by taking away some of the tiles. Then they let him down on his cot into the crowd of people in front of Jesus. When Jesus saw how much faith they had, he said to the man, "My friend, your sins are forgiven."

The teachers of the Scriptures and those who strictly obeyed the rules of their religion began to say to themselves, "Who does this man think he is? Only God can forgive sins. This man has done a terrible thing. He claims to be equal with God."

Jesus knew what they were thinking, and so he said to them, "Why do you think such things? Is it easier for me to say, 'Your sins are forgiven' or to say, 'Get up and walk'? I will now prove to you that God's Chosen Man has the right to forgive people who sin." So he said to the crippled man, "Get up! Pick up your cot and go home!"

At once the man got up while everyone was looking on. He picked up his cot and went home, praising God. The people who saw Jesus heal the man were completely amazed, and they were also very much afraid. They said, "Praise God! We have seen wonderful things happen today!"

What Makes God Displeased with a Person

On another day some teachers of the Scriptures and those who strictly obeyed the teaching of their ancestors came from Jerusalem to see Jesus. They said to him, "Our ancestors taught us to wash our hands in a certain way before we eat. Why don't your followers obey the teaching of our ancestors?"

Jesus answered, "And why don't you obey the teaching of God? Why do you disobey him and follow your own teaching? You know that God said, 'Respect your father and mother,' and you also know that he said, 'Put to death anyone who curses his father and mother.' But you teach that a person does not have to respect his parents. So that a man won't have to give help to his parents you let him say, 'What I own belongs to God.' In this way you disobey God and follow your own teaching. You only pretend to obey God. What the prophet Isaiah said long ago about people like you is true. He said, 'You people say that you honour God, but you do not really love him. It's no use for you to worship God. You teach people to obey your rules, and you pretend that they are God's rules.' "

After that, Jesus called the crowd to him and said, "Listen to me and try to understand what I say. It is not what a person puts into his mouth that makes God displeased with him. What goes out of a person's mouth is what makes God displeased."

Then Jesus' followers came to him and said, "Do you know that the men who strictly obey the teaching of their ancestors got their feelings hurt by what you said?"

Jesus answered, "These men are like plants which my Father in heaven did not plant, and every one of them will be pulled up. Don't worry about them. They are like blind people trying to lead other blind people. And when one blind person leads another, they both fall into a ditch."

Peter spoke up, "Tell us what you meant when you talked about what makes God displeased with a person."

Jesus said to his followers, "You still don't know any more than the others. Can't you understand? Food that a person puts into his mouth goes into his stomach and then out of his body. But the things that come out of a person's mouth come from his heart, and these are the things that can displease God. Evil thoughts come from a person's heart, and they are what lead a man to murder people, to be untrue to his wife, and to do all kinds of filthy things. These evil thoughts also cause a person to rob, lie and say bad things about others. All these things make God displeased with a person. But to eat without washing your hands in the right way is not what displeases God."

A Sinful Woman

Once a man named Simon, who was a teacher of the Jewish religion, invited Jesus to have dinner with him. A sinful woman who lived in that town heard that Jesus was at the man's house. So she took an expensive jar of perfume and went there while Jesus and all the other guests were eating. She stood by Jesus. She cried, and her tears fell on his feet. Then she dried his feet with her hair, kissed them, and poured the perfume on them.

When Simon saw this, he said to himself, "This man cannot be a prophet. A prophet would know what kind of woman is touching him. He would know what a sinful person she is."

Jesus spoke up and said, "Simon, I have something to tell you."

"Yes, Teacher," he said, "what is it?"

Then Jesus told him a story about two men who owed money to another man. He said, "One man owed him 500 silver coins, and the other man owed him 50 silver coins. Neither of them had any money, so he told both of them that they did not have to pay him back. Simon, which one of the men do you think will be more grateful?"

Simon answered, "I think that the one who was forgiven more will be more grateful."

Jesus answered, "You are right." Then he turned to the woman and said to Simon, "Do you see this woman? I came into your home, but you did not give me any water to wash my feet. Yet she has washed my feet with her tears and dried them with her hair. You did not welcome me with a kiss, but she has not stopped kissing my feet since I came in. You did not pour any olive oil on my head, but she has covered my feet with perfume. I tell you, then, that her many sins are forgiven. She has shown this by her love. But whoever has been forgiven little shows only a little love."

Then Jesus said to the woman, "Your sins are forgiven."

The other guests at the table began to say to one another, "Who is this man to declare that a person's sins are forgiven?"

But Jesus said to the woman, "Your faith has saved you. Go home in peace."

The Lost Sheep

One day many tax collectors and other sinful people came to hear Jesus teach. So the religious leaders of the Jews complained. They said, "This man welcomes sinners and even eats with them!"

Then Jesus said to the men who had complained, "If one of you has a hundred sheep and loses one of them, what would you do? You would leave the other ninety-nine sheep in the field and go look for the one that got lost until you found it. When you found the sheep, you would put it on your shoulder and carry it back home. You would be so happy that you would call all your friends and neighbours together and say to them, 'I'm so happy that I found my lost sheep. Let's celebrate!'"

Then Jesus said to the people, "That is the way it is in heaven. God is happier over one sinner who turns from his sin, than he is over ninety-nine others who do not think that they need to turn from their sins."

Jesus Teaches on a Hill

Crowds of people were following Jesus. One day he went up a hill where he could sit down to teach them. His followers gathered around him, and he said to them,

"You are indeed happy if you know how much you need God;
  you can enjoy life under God's rule.
You are indeed happy if you suffer with people who suffer;
  God will take away your sorrow.

34

You are indeed happy if you humbly follow God;
  God will give you the whole world.
You are indeed happy if you love to obey God;
  God will make that love possible.
You are indeed happy if you show mercy to others;
  God will show mercy to you.
You are indeed happy if you let God live in your heart;
  you will see him.
You are indeed happy if you bring peace between people;
  God will call you his children.
You are indeed happy if you suffer because you obey God;
  you can enjoy life under God's rule."

Jesus Feeds Five Thousand Men

When Jesus heard about the death of John the Baptist, he wanted to go some place where he could be alone. He got in a boat and went to a lonely place on the other side of Lake Galilee. The people heard that Jesus was going to the other side of the lake, so they left their towns and followed him by land. When Jesus got out of the boat, he saw a large crowd and the sick people they had brought with them. He felt sorry for them and healed all the sick people.

That evening Jesus' followers came to him and said, "It is already very late, and the people are far from home. Why don't you tell them to go to the villages and buy some food?"

Jesus answered, "They don't have to leave. You can give them something to eat."

But Jesus' followers said, "All we have are five loaves of bread and two fish!"

Jesus told his followers to bring him the bread and the fish, and then he told all the people to sit down on the grass. Jesus took the five loaves and the two fish, looked up to heaven, and gave thanks to God. He broke the loaves of bread and gave the pieces to his followers. His followers then gave them to the people. Everyone ate until they had all they wanted. After that, Jesus' followers took up twelve baskets full of what was left over. There were about five thousand men who ate, not counting the women and children.

Jesus Walks on the Water

After Jesus had fed the five thousand men, he made his followers get into a boat and go back to the other side of Lake Galilee   Jesus also sent home the crowd of people who had followed him. Then he went up a hill to pray by himself. When night came, Jesus was still there alone. But the boat was far out on the lake, tossed about by the waves, because the wind was blowing against it.

Sometime between three and six o'clock in the morning, Jesus came near the boat. He was walking on the water, and when his followers saw him, they were frightened. "It's a ghost," they said, and they screamed with fear.

Jesus at once said, "Don't be afraid! It's me. There's no need to be frightened."

Then Peter spoke up, "Lord, if it is really you, tell me to walk to you on the water!"

"Come here!" Jesus told him. So Peter got out of the boat and began walking on the water to Jesus. But when he saw how strong the wind was, he was afraid and started to sink down in the water. "Save me, Lord!" he shouted.

At once Jesus reached out and grabbed hold of him and said, "You have such little faith! Why didn't you believe me?"

They both got into the boat, and the wind stopped blowing so hard. Then Jesus' followers in the boat worshipped him and said, "You really are the Son of God!"

The Transfiguration

Jesus took Peter, James, and John with him and went up a hill to pray. While he was praying, a change came over his face, and his clothes became shining white. Suddenly, two men were there talking with him. The men were Moses and Elijah, and their clothes also shone with splendour. They were talking with Jesus about God's purpose for him and about his coming death in Jerusalem. Peter and the two other followers were sound asleep. But they woke up and saw Jesus in all of his glory and the two men who were standing with him. As the men were leaving Jesus, Peter said to him, "Master, it is good for us to be here! We will put up three tents, one for you, one for Moses, and one for Elijah." (Peter did not really know what he was talking about.)

While Peter was still speaking, a cloud came and covered them with its shadow. Jesus' followers were afraid. Then a voice from the cloud said, "This is my Son, whom I have chosen. Listen to him!"

When the voice stopped speaking, Peter, James, and John saw Jesus standing there all alone. They kept quiet about what had happened, and they did not tell anyone what they had seen until after Jesus was raised from death.

The Samaritan Woman

One day Jesus and his followers left the land of Judea and started back to the land of Galilee. But to get there, they had to go through the land of Samaria.

As Jesus and his followers were going through Samaria, they came to a town named Sychar. This town was not far from the field that Jacob (the ancestor of the Jews and the Samaritans) had given to his son Joseph many years earlier. Near the town was a well, called Jacob's well. And since Jesus was tired after walking, he sat down by the well to rest. It was now about noon, and Jesus sat there alone while his followers went into town to buy food.

While Jesus was sitting there, a Samaritan woman came to the well to get some water. Jesus said to her, "Please give me a drink of water."

"How can you ask me for a drink?" the woman answered. "You are a Jew and I am a Samaritan, and I thought that Jews did not like Samaritans and would not use the same cups and bowls that Samaritans use."

Jesus answered, "You do not know the gift that only God can give, and you do not know who it is that is asking you for a drink. If you did, you would have asked me for a drink, and I would have given you water that makes people live."

"Sir," the woman said, "you don't have a bucket or a rope, and the well is deep. Where are you going to get that water that makes people live? Our ancestor Jacob dug this well for us long ago. He and his sons drank water from it during their lifetime, and they gave their animals water from it. Do you think you are greater than our ancestor Jacob?"

Jesus answered, "Everyone who drinks the water from this well will get thirsty again, but whoever drinks the water that I will give him will never be thirsty again. The water that I will give him will become like a spring of water inside of him. It will keep on giving him water that will make him live; it will give him eternal life."

The woman said, "Sir, please give me some of that water. Then I will never get thirsty again, and I will not have to come back to this well to get water."

"Go get your husband," Jesus told her, "and then come back here."

"I don't have a husband," she answered.

Jesus spoke again and said, "You are right when you say that you don't have a husband. You don't have one now, but you have been married to five men, and you are now living with a man that you are not married to. So you told me the truth."

"Sir," the woman said, "since you know all that about me, you must be a prophet that God has sent to us. My Samaritan ancestors worshipped God on the top of Mount Gerizim, that mountain over there. But you Jews say that the city of Jerusalem is the place where we should worship God."

Jesus said to her, "Believe me, the time will come when people will no longer worship God the Father on that mountain there or in Jerusalem. You Samaritans do not really know the God whom you worship. But we Jews know him. We know him because God will save the world through the Jews. But the time is coming, and in fact it is already here, when the Spirit of God will lead people to worship the Father as he really is. They will worship him in the way that he wants to be worshipped. God is Spirit, and people can worship him as he really is only when God's Spirit leads them."

The woman said to him, "I know that God's Chosen King will someday come. And when he does, he will tell us everything."

Jesus answered, "I am that man. You are talking with him now."

Just then Jesus' followers came back. When they saw Jesus talking with a woman, they were surprised, but none of them asked the woman what she wanted. And no one asked Jesus why he was talking with her.

Then the woman left her water jar there at the well and ran back to town. She said to the people, "Come and see the man who told me everything I have ever done. Do you think he could be the Chosen King?" When the people heard what the woman said, they started out to the well where Jesus was.

While all this was happening, Jesus' followers were asking him to eat something. "Teacher," they were saying, "please have something to eat."

But he answered, "I have food to eat that you know nothing about." So they asked one another if anyone else could have brought him some food.

Then Jesus said to them, "The only food I need is to obey God, who sent me into the world, and to finish the work that he gave me to do. You say that it takes four months from the time you plant the seed to the time you gather the crops. But take a good look at the fields now. You will see that the crops are already ripe and ready to be gathered. Everyone who works in the fields to gather the crops is paid for his work. But what I am really talking about is the food which God gives to those who obey him, and everyone who works in God's fields is gathering the kind of food that gives eternal life. The people who obey God and plant the seed and the people who obey God and gather the crops will celebrate together. It is true that one person plants the seed and someone else gathers the crops. I have sent you to gather crops in a field where you did not work to plant the seed. Other people worked there to plant the seed, and you have the joy of gathering the crops that they planted.

Many of the Samaritans in that town believed that Jesus was the Chosen King. They believed because the woman had said, "He told me everything I have ever done." So when the Samaritans came to Jesus, they begged him to stay on with them. And Jesus stayed there two days.

Many more of the Samaritans believed that Jesus was the Chosen King because of what he told them. They said to the woman, "We believe now, not because of what you said, but because we have heard him teach. We know that he really is the one God has sent to save the world."

Jesus and the Children

One day some people brought their children to Jesus for him to place his hands on them and give them his blessing. His followers saw the people doing this and tried to send them away. But Jesus called the children to him and said, ''Let the children come to me. Do not stop them, because people who come to God like children will enjoy his rule! Remember this! You cannot enjoy God's rule, if you do not come to him like a child.''

The Lord's Prayer

Many people thought that God would hear them because they prayed long prayers. So Jesus taught his followers how to pray. This is the prayer that he taught them:

"Our Father in heaven,
  We pray that all people will honour you.
  We pray that you will be the king of this world,
    and that people on earth will obey you,
      even as you are obeyed in heaven.
  Give us the food that we need for today.
  Forgive us for the wrong things that we have done,
    as we forgive others for the wrong things
      that they do to us.
  Do not let the Devil put us to the test,
    but keep us safe from his power."

The Friend at Midnight

As Jesus was teaching his followers about prayer, he said, "Suppose one of you should go to your neighbour's house at midnight and ask, 'Can I borrow a few pieces of bread? A friend of mine has travelled here to see me, and I don't have any food for him.' At first your neighbour might answer, 'Go away! The door is locked, and my family and I are already in bed. I can't get up and give you anything.' But what will happen if you keep on asking him for the bread? I'll tell you what will happen. Your neighbour will finally get up and give you everything you need. He will do this, not because you are his friend, but because you are not ashamed to keep on asking.

That is how you should pray. Keep on asking God, and you will receive. Keep on looking, and you will find. Keep on knocking, and God will open the door for you. When your son asks you for a fish to eat, do you give him a snake? When he asks for an egg, do you give him a scorpion? Of course not! As bad as you are, you give your children the things that are good for them. But your Father in heaven does far more than that. He gives his Spirit to those who ask him."

Zacchaeus

As Jesus was on his way to Jerusalem, he was passing through the town of Jericho. A man by the name of Zacchaeus lived there. He was a chief tax collector and was very rich. He wanted to get a look at Jesus, to see what he was like. But Zacchaeus was a little man, and he could not see Jesus because of the crowd. So he ran on ahead and climbed a sycamore tree. When Jesus passed that way, he looked up at Zacchaeus in the tree and said, "Hurry down, Zacchaeus. I'm going to stay at your house today."

He hurried down and welcomed Jesus. Zacchaeus was very happy, but everyone else was angry and said, "Look! This man Jesus has gone to be the guest of a sinner."

During the meal Zacchaeus stood up and said to Jesus, "Lord, I'm going to give half of everything I own to the poor. And if I have cheated anyone, I will pay him back four times as much."

Then Jesus said to him, "Today God has saved you and your family. You are a true descendant of Abraham. I have come to look for you that are lost and to save you."

The Rich Man and the Poor Man

The Jewish religious leaders loved money. So Jesus told them this story:

There was once a rich man who always dressed in the most expensive clothes and lived in great luxury. There was also a poor man named Lazarus who was brought to the rich man's door every day to beg for the scraps of food that were thrown away from his table. Lazarus was covered with sores and was so helpless that even the dogs of the street came and licked his sores.

The poor man died, and God's angels carried him to the banquet in heaven. There he was seated beside Abraham, the famous ancestor of the Jews.

The rich man also died and was buried. In the world of the dead he was in great pain. He looked up and saw Abraham far away, with Lazarus sitting at his side. So he called out, "Father Abraham! Take pity on me. Send Lazarus to dip his finger in some water and cool off my tongue. I am in great pain here in this fire!"

Abraham answered, "Remember that during your lifetime you had everything you wanted, while everything that was bad happened to Lazarus. But now he is enjoying himself here, while you are in pain. And besides all that, there is a deep pit between us. From where we are, no one can go to you; and from where you are, no one can come to us."

Then the rich man said, "In that case, father Abraham, I beg you to send Lazarus back to my home, where my five brothers are still living. Let him go and warn them, so that they will not also come to this place of pain."

Abraham said, "Your brothers can read what Moses and the prophets wrote. Your brothers should pay attention to what is written there."

The rich man answered, "That is not enough, father Abraham! But if someone would come back from the world of the dead and go to them, they would turn away from their sins."

But Abraham said, "If they will not listen to what Moses and the prophets wrote, they will not believe the truth even if someone comes back from death."

The Story of the Lost Son

When Jesus was here on earth, some of the people did not like him, because he often ate with people they thought were sinful. So Jesus told them this story about a man who had two grown sons:

One day the younger son said to his father, "Father, give me my share of what you own. It will belong to my brother and to me after you die, and I would rather have my part now." So the man divided what he owned between his two sons.

In just a few days, the younger son sold everything that his father had given him. He left home with the money and went to a country that was far away. There he spent his money foolishly and lived without a care for the future. He spent everything that he had. But a time came when there was not enough food in that country, and he began to go hungry. So he went to work for one of the men who lived there. The man sent him out to his farm to take care of the pigs. The boy was so hungry that he wanted to eat the bean pods that he was feeding to the pigs, but no one would let him have any.

At last he came to his senses and said to himself, "All the hired workers on my father's farm have more than they can eat, and here I am about to starve to death. I will go back to my father right now and say, 'Father, what I did was wrong; I have sinned against God and against you. I am not good enough any longer even to be called your son. Give me a job as one of your hired workers and treat me like one of them.'" So he started back home to his father.

He was still a long way from the house when his father saw him. His heart was filled with love for his son, and he ran to him, hugged him, and kissed him. "Father," the son said, "what I did was wrong; I have sinned against God and against you. I am not good enough any longer even to be called your son."

But before the son could finish speaking, his father called to his servants and said, "Hurry! Bring the best robe that I own, and put it on him. Put one of my rings on his finger and get some shoes for him. Then go and kill the calf that we have been saving for a special feast. Cook it, and we will have a big party to celebrate the return of my son. I thought my son was dead, but he has come back alive; he was lost, but now he has been found." So the party began.

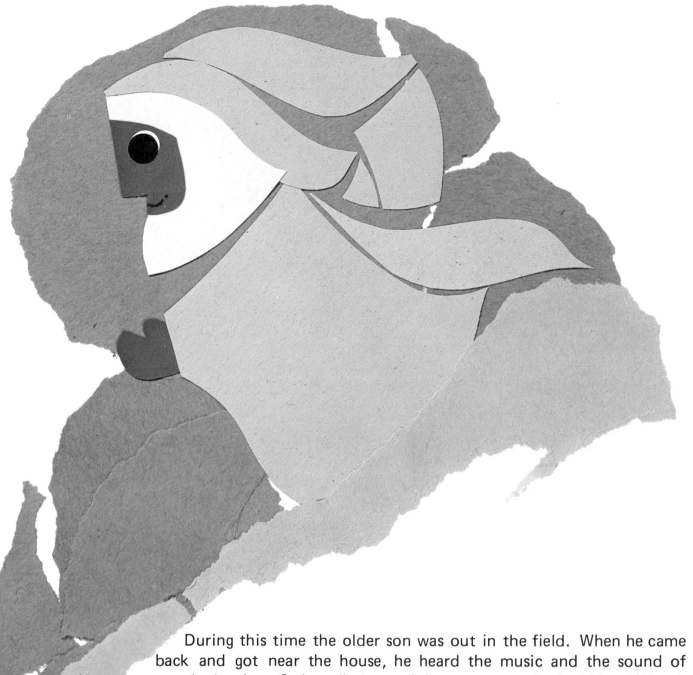

During this time the older son was out in the field. When he came back and got near the house, he heard the music and the sound of people dancing. So he called one of the servants and asked him, "What's going on here?"

"Your brother has come back home," the servant answered, "and your father has killed the calf we have been saving. He is having a big party because his son came back safe and sound."

But the older son was too angry even to go into the house; so his father went out and begged him to come in. But he refused. He said, "Look, I've worked like a slave for you all these years and I've never disobeyed you. Yet you have never given me anything, not even a goat, so that I could have a party with my friends. But this son of yours came back after he had spent all your money on evil women. And for a son like that you have killed the best calf we have!"

"My son," the father answered, "you are always here with me, and everything I have is yours. But we had to have a party and celebrate because your brother has come home. He was dead, but now he is alive; he was lost, but now he has been found."

The Story of the Good Samaritan

One time a man who knew the Scriptures well came to Jesus and tried to trap him by asking him a question. "Teacher," he asked, "what must I do to receive the eternal life that God gives?"

Jesus answered him by asking, "What do the Scriptures teach? How do you understand what they say?"

The man answered by quoting from the Scriptures: "Love the Lord your God with all your heart. Love him in everything that you do or think or feel," and "love others as much as you love yourself."

"You are right," Jesus answered. "If you do this you will have eternal life."

But the man wanted to show that he had been right in asking the question, so he said to Jesus, "But who are these others that I must love?"

Jesus answered, "There was once a man who was travelling from Jerusalem down to the town of Jericho. On the way he was attacked by robbers. They beat him up and took everything he had, including his clothes, and then left him lying in the road, almost dead. It happened that a priest was also going down that road. When he came to the man and saw him lying there, he moved to the other side of the road and walked by. After that, a man who helped the priests do their work in the Temple came along the road where the man was lying. He went over and looked at him, but then walked right on by. A little later, a Samaritan was travelling that way, and he came to where the man was lying. But when this Samaritan foreigner saw the injured man, he felt sorry for him. He went over to the man and used olive oil and wine as medicine on the man's wounds. When he had bandaged the wounds, he put the man on his own donkey and took him to an inn. He stayed with him and took care of him all night long. The next day he paid the bill and then took out two more silver coins and gave them to the innkeeper. "Here," he said, "take care of this man, and if you spend any more than this, I will pay you when I come back this way."

Then Jesus looked at the man who had tried to trap him with a question. Jesus asked him, "What do you think? Which one of these three showed love to the man who was attacked by robbers?"

The man answered Jesus, "The one who was kind to him."

"So then," Jesus said, "go and love others in that way."

Proud People and Humble People

There were some people who felt sure that God was pleased with them, and they looked down on everyone else. So Jesus told them this story. Two men went to the Temple in Jerusalem to pray. One of them was a man who strictly obeyed the rules of his religion. The other was a tax collector. The religious man stood up where everyone could see him and prayed, "O God, I thank you that I am not like everyone else. I am not greedy or dishonest, and I am faithful to my wife. I thank you that I am not like that tax collector over there. I do more than you command. Each week I go without food for two days, and I give you one-tenth of all that I earn."

"But the tax collector stood off to the side and was too ashamed even to look up toward heaven. He beat his chest with his fist to show that he was sorry for his sins. He said, "O God, have pity on me. I am a sinner."

Then Jesus said to the people, "Listen! When the tax collector left the Temple, God was pleased with him, but he was not pleased with the other man. God will put to shame everyone who is proud of himself, but he will give a place of honour to everyone who admits that he is a sinner."

Jesus Heals a Blind Man

As Jesus and his followers were walking along through the city of Jerusalem, they saw a man who had been born blind. Jesus' followers asked him, ''Teacher, why was this man born blind? Was it because he sinned or because his parents sinned?''

Jesus answered, ''Neither his sins nor his parents' sins have anything to do with his blindness. He is blind so that God can show his power and heal him. As long as it is day, we must do the work of God, who sent me into the world. Night is coming when no one can work. While I am in the world, I bring light to the world.''

After Jesus had said this, he spat on the ground and made some mud with the spit. He rubbed the mud on the man's eyes, then said to him, ''Go and wash your face in the Pool of Siloam.'' (The name Siloam means ''Sent.'') The man went and washed his face, and when he came back, he could see.

Then his neighbours and the people who had seen him begging asked one another, ''Isn't he the man who used to sit and beg?'' Some of the people said, ''Yes,'' but others said, ''No, he just looks like him.''

But the man himself said, ''I am the one who used to sit and beg.''

The people then asked him, ''How is it that you can now see?''

He answered, ''The man named Jesus made some mud, rubbed it on my eyes, and told me to go to the Pool of Siloam and wash my face. I went, and as soon as I had washed my face, I could see.''

''Where is that man?'' they asked.

He answered, ''I don't know.''

The day on which Jesus healed the man was a Sabbath, the Jewish day of worship. (The Jews had laws about what could be done on the Sabbath.) So the people took the man to those who strictly obeyed the rules of their religion, and they asked him how he got his sight back. The man told them, ''Jesus put some mud on my eyes. I washed my face, and now I can see.''

Then some of them said, ''The man who did that could not have come from God, because he does not obey the laws about the Sabbath.''

But others said, ''How could a man who is a sinner do such miracles as that?'' And they couldn't agree about Jesus.

So they asked the blind man once more, "Do you still say that this man cured you of your blindness? Well then, what do you think about him?"

"He is a prophet," the man answered.

But they were not willing to believe that he had been blind and could now see. So they called his parents and asked them, "Is this your son? Was he born blind? Then how can he see now?"

His parents answered, "We know that he is our son, and we know that he was born blind. But we don't know how it is that he can now see or who cured him of his blindness. Why don't you ask him? He is old enough to answer for himself." His parents said this because they were afraid that the Jewish leaders would put them out of the synagogue. The Jewish leaders had already said that they would do this to anyone who believed that Jesus was God's Chosen King.

So they called the man back the second time and said to him, "Promise before God that you will tell the truth! We know that this man who healed you is a sinner."

"I do not know if he is a sinner or not," the man answered. "I only know that I was blind, and now I can see!"

"What did he do to you?" they asked. "How did he heal you?"

"I have already told you," he answered, "and you would not listen to me. Why do you want to hear it again? Do you also want to become his followers?"

Then they insulted him. They said, "You are a follower of that man named Jesus, but we follow the teachings of Moses. We know that God spoke to Moses, but we do not even know where that man Jesus comes from."

The man answered, "That certainly is strange! You don't know where he comes from, but he cured me of my blindness! We know that God does not answer the prayers of sinners. He only answers the prayers of people who honour him and do what he wants them to do. This is the first time since the beginning of the world that anyone has heard of a person giving sight to a man who was born blind. If this man Jesus did not come from God, he would not be able to do anything."

The Jewish leaders answered, "You were born and raised a sinner. What makes you think you have the right to teach us?" And they put him out of the synagogue.

When Jesus heard what the Jewish leaders had done to the man, he found him and asked him, "Do you put your trust in God's Chosen Man?"

He answered, "Sir, tell me who he is, so that I can put my trust in him." Jesus said to him, "You have already seen him. He is the one who is talking with you now."

"I put my trust in you, Lord!" the man said, and he knelt down to worship Jesus.

Jesus said, "I came into this world to be a judge, so that people who are blind could see and people who see would become blind."

Some of the men there heard Jesus say this, and they asked him, "Do you think we are blind too?" Jesus answered, "If you were really blind, you would not be guilty of sin. But you claim that you can see, and that means that you are still guilty of sin."

Jesus Uses Stories to Teach

One day Jesus left the house and went to the shore of Lake Galilee, where he sat down to teach. Such a large crowd of people gathered around him that it was difficult for him to speak. So he got into a boat and sat down in it, while the crowd stood on the shore. He used stories to teach them many things.

The Story about Seeds

Jesus said, "A man went out to plant grain by scattering seed over his field.

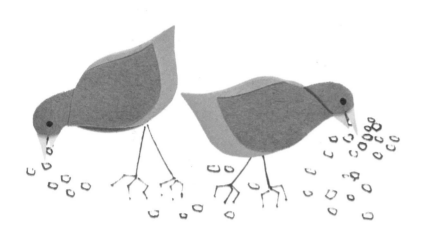

Some of the seed fell on the path that went alongside the field, and the birds came and ate it up.

Some of it fell on rocky ground where the soil was not very deep. The seed soon sprouted, but when the sun got hot, it burned the young plants.

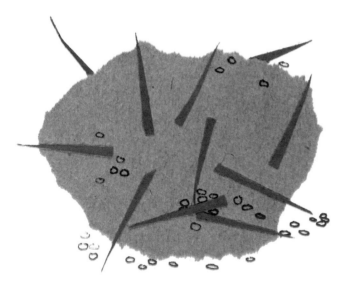

Some of the seed fell in places where there were roots of thorn bushes. As soon as the thorn bushes grew up, they choked the young plants.

But some of the seed fell on good soil, and the plants grew and produced a lot of grain. Some of the plants produced one hundred grains, others produced sixty, and others thirty."

When Jesus finished the story, he said, "You have heard what I said. Pay attention!"

Jesus Explains the Story about the Seeds

Jesus went on teaching his followers and said, "Now listen and learn what the story about the seeds means. Some people hear the good news about how God rules the world, but they do not understand it. They are like the seeds that fell on the path. Just as the birds came and ate the seeds, the Devil comes and takes away what they heard.

"Some people hear what is said and as soon as they hear, they accept it gladly. They are like the seeds that fell on rocky ground and had little soil. What they hear does not take root in their hearts, and it is soon forgotten. So when troubles come or they have to suffer because of what they believe, they give up at once.

"Some people hear what is said, but they are like the seeds that grew among thorn bushes. They worry about this life, and they love money so much that they never think about what they heard. The seeds do not grow and produce grain.

"But some people hear the good news. They understand it and obey it. They are like the seeds that fell on good soil. They grow up and produce grain; some produce one hundred grains, some produce sixty, and some thirty."

The Good Wheat and the Weeds

On that same day Jesus told his followers some other stories about how God rules this world. Jesus said, "A man planted good wheat in his field. But one night when everyone was asleep, an enemy came and scattered weed seeds in the field where the wheat was planted. When the plants grew and the grain began to form the weeds also came up. The man's workers came to him and said, 'Sir, didn't you plant good wheat that was not mixed with weed seeds? Where did the weeds come from?'

" 'It was an enemy who did this,' he answered.

" 'Do you want us to go and pull up the weeds?' they asked him.

" 'No,' he answered, 'because if you pull up the weeds you will also pull up some of the wheat with them. Let the wheat and the weeds grow in the same field until it is time to gather the wheat. Then I will tell the workers to pull up the weeds first, tie them in bundles, and burn them. After they have done that, they will gather the wheat and put it in my barn.' "

Jesus Explains the Story about the Weeds

Jesus left the crowds and went into the house. His followers came to him and said, "Tell us the meaning of the story about the weeds in the field."

Jesus answered, "The man who planted the good wheat is God's Chosen Man. The field in which he planted the seed is the world. The good seed stands for the people who belong to God and obey him. The weeds stand for the people who belong to the Devil. He is the enemy who scattered the weed seeds in the field. The time for gathering the wheat stands for the end of this world. The men who gathered the wheat are the angels. You heard how the weeds were gathered up and burned in the fire. The same thing will happen to all of the bad people at the end of the world. God's Chosen Man will send out his angels to take away all the bad people. The angels will gather up all evil people and all those who cause others to sin. The angels will throw them into the burning furnace, where they will cry out in great pain. Then God's people will shine like the sun in the Kingdom of God their Father. You have heard what I said. Pay attention!"

The Story about the Tiny Mustard Seed

Jesus then told them another story about how God rules this world. "A man takes a tiny mustard seed and plants it in his field. It is the smallest of all seeds, but when it grows up, it is the biggest of all plants. It becomes a tree, large enough for birds to make their nests in its branches."

The Story about Yeast

Jesus told them still another story. "A woman takes some yeast and mixes it with a bushel of flour. She makes dough, and the yeast makes the whole batch of dough rise."

The Reason Jesus Used Stories

Jesus used these stories to teach the crowds about how God rules this world. He did not tell them anything without using a story to explain it. He did this to make come true what the prophet has said:

"I will use stories when I speak to them.
I will tell them things that no one
has ever known."

The Story about a Hidden Treasure

Jesus also told his followers still other stories about how God rules this world. "A man found a treasure hidden in a field. He was very happy. So he covered it up again and went and sold everything he owned. He then came back and bought the field."

The Story about the Pearl

Jesus said, "A man who was looking for fine pearls found one that was very valuable. So he sold everything he owned to buy that pearl."

The Story about the Net

Jesus said, "One day some fishermen let down their large net in the lake and caught all kinds of fish. When the net was full, they pulled it to shore and sat down to divide the fish. They put the good fish in buckets and threw away all the fish that could not be eaten. That is the way it will be at the end of this world. The angels will go and gather up all the evil people from among the good people. Then they will throw the evil people into the burning furnace, where they will cry out in great pain."

New Truths and Old

Jesus asked his followers, "Do you understand all these things?"

"Yes," they answered.

Then he said to them, "This means that every teacher of the Scriptures who has learned how God rules in this world is like a home owner who takes new things and old things out of his storeroom."

Jesus is not Welcomed in His Home Town

When Jesus finished teaching, he left and went back to his home town. He taught in the synagogue there, and those who heard him were amazed. "Where did he get such wisdom?" they asked. "And what about his miracles? Isn't he the carpenter's son? Isn't Mary his mother, and aren't James, Joseph, Simon, and Judas his brothers? Aren't all his sisters living here? Where did he get all this?" So they did not welcome him.

Jesus said to them, "A prophet is honoured everywhere except in his home town and by his own family." Because the people did not put their faith in Jesus, he did not perform many miracles there.

Lazarus is Brought Back to Life

The Death of Lazarus

A man named Lazarus lived in Bethany in the land of Judea. Bethany was the town where Mary and her sister Martha lived. Mary was the woman who had poured perfume on Jesus' feet and wiped them with her hair. Lazarus was their brother, and he became sick. So the two sisters sent Jesus a message: "Lord, your dear friend Lazarus is sick."

When Jesus heard this, he said, "This sickness will not end with the death of Lazarus. God will use it to show his wonderful power. You will also see the wonderful power of his Son."

Jesus loved Lazarus and his two sisters. Yet when he heard the news that Lazarus was sick, he stayed where he was for two more days. Then he said to his followers, "Let's go back to Judea."

"Teacher, " his followers answered, "just a short time ago the people there wanted to stone you to death. Why are you planning to go back?"

Jesus said, "Each day has twelve hours of daylight, doesn't it? So whoever walks in the daytime does not stumble, because he has light to see by. But if he walks at night, he stumbles because he has no light." Jesus also said, "Our friend Lazarus has fallen asleep, but I will go and wake him up."

His followers answered, "If he is just sleeping, he will get well."

But when Jesus said, "Lazarus has fallen asleep," he meant that he had died. His followers did not understand this and thought he meant that Lazarus was just sleeping. So Jesus told them plainly "Lazarus is dead. I am glad that I was not there when he died, because now you will believe. Let's go to him."

One of Jesus' followers was named Thomas, and he was also called the Twin. Thomas said to the others, "Let's all go to Judea with the Teacher and die there with him."

Jesus Has the Power to Give Life

Bethany was less than two miles from Jerusalem, and many of the people from Jerusalem and that region came to comfort Martha and Mary. When Jesus got to Bethany, he found that Lazarus had already been buried four days.

Martha heard that Jesus was coming, and she went out to meet him, but Mary stayed in the house. Martha said to Jesus, "If you had been here, Lord, my brother would not have died! But I know even now that God will answer your prayers and do whatever you ask him."

"Your brother will come back to life," Jesus told her.

She answered, "I know that he will come back to life at the end of the world, when people are brought back from death." Jesus said to her, "I am the one who brings people back from death and gives them life. Whoever puts his trust in me will live, even if he dies; and whoever lives and trusts me will never die. Do you believe this?"

"Yes, Lord, I do believe that you are God's Chosen King. You are God's Son that he promised to send into the world."

Jesus Weeps

After Martha said this, she went back to the house and called her sister Mary. "The Teacher is here," she whispered, "and he is asking for you." Mary hurried out to meet Jesus. He had not yet reached the village, but was still in the place where Martha had met him. Everyone who had come to comfort Mary got up and followed her when they saw her hurry out. They thought she was going to the tomb to weep there.

When Mary saw Jesus, she bowed down at his feet and said, "If you had been here, Lord, my brother would not have died!"

Jesus saw that she was crying and that many of the people with her were also crying. Jesus was deeply concerned and he asked, "Where have you buried him?"

"Come and see, Lord," they answered.

Jesus wept.

"See how much he loved him!" some of the people said.

But others said, "He gave sight to a blind man, didn't he? Couldn't he have kept Lazarus from dying?"

Lazarus is Brought Back to Life

Jesus was deeply concerned about what had happened. He went to the tomb, which was a cave with a stone placed at the opening. "Take away the stone!" Jesus ordered.

But Martha, who was Lazarus' sister, answered, "There will be a bad smell, Lord. He has been buried four days!"

Jesus said to her, "Didn't I tell you that you would see God's wonderful power, if you believed?" They rolled the stone away. Jesus looked up toward heaven and prayed, "I thank you, Father, that you listen to me when I pray. I know that you always listen to me, but I am saying this now so that the people will understand and believe that you sent me." After he prayed, he called out in a loud voice, "Lazarus, come out!" And Lazarus came out of the grave. His hands and his feet were wrapped with cloths that were used to wrap the dead. He also had a cloth tied around his face. "Untie him," Jesus told them, "and let him go."

The Enemies of Jesus

The chief priests and the men who strictly obeyed the rules of their religion heard what Jesus had done, so they called together the Jewish Council in Jerusalem. They asked one another, "What shall we do? Look at all the miracles this man is performing! If we let him go on like this, every one will put their trust in him. Then the Romans will send their armies to destroy our Temple and nation!"

One of the members of the Council was named Caiaphas, and he was the High Priest that year. Caiaphas said, "What fools you are. Don't you know that it is better to let one man die for the people, rather than have the whole nation destroyed?" He really didn't say this because he had thought of it himself. But he said it because, as High Priest that year, God had used him to tell ahead of time that Jesus was going to die for the Jewish people. He was going to die for them and for all the other people of God scattered in many nations. His death would bring all of God's people together in one family.

Beginning with that day, the Jewish leaders made plans to kill Jesus. So Jesus no longer travelled openly in Judea. He left and went to a town named Ephraim, near the desert, where he stayed with his followers.

The time for the Passover Festival was near, and many people from the country came to Jerusalem. They came to do the things that their religion required them to do in order to purify themselves for the Passover Festival. As they gathered in the Temple, they were looking for Jesus, and they asked one another, "What do you think? You don't think he will come to the festival, do you?" The chief priests and the religious leaders wanted to arrest Jesus. So they had given orders that anyone who knew where Jesus was must let them know.

Jesus Enters Jerusalem

Jesus was leading his followers toward Jerusalem, and he was teaching them as they went. When he came to the towns of Bethphage and Bethany near the Mount of Olives, he sent two of his followers ahead of him. He instructed them, "Go into town, and there you will find a colt tied up that no one has ever ridden. Untie it and bring it here. If anyone asks you why you are doing this, tell him that the Master needs it."

Jesus' two followers went and found everything just as he had told them. As they were untying the colt, its owners asked them, "Why are you taking the colt?"

"The Master needs it," they answered, and they took the colt to Jesus. Then Jesus' followers threw their coats on the back of the animal and helped Jesus get on it. As he rode along, people spread their coats on the road in front of him.

A large crowd of his followers was with him when he came to the place near Jerusalem, where the road goes down the Mount of Olives. They began to thank God and praise him with loud voices for all the great things that they had seen. They shouted, "God bless the King who comes in the name of the Lord! Peace in heaven! Praise God!"

Some of those who strictly obeyed the teaching of their ancestors were there. So they said to Jesus, "Teacher, tell your followers to be quiet!"

Jesus answered, "I tell you that if they keep quiet, the stones will start shouting."

Jesus came closer to Jerusalem. He looked at the city and wept over it. He said, "I wish you knew today what would bring peace to your people. But you cannot see it! The time will come when your enemies will have armies all around you. They will build battle walls and shut you in so that there is no way to escape. They will completely destroy you and the people inside your walls. They will not even leave one stone in place. You are going to be destroyed because you do not know that God is here to save you."

79

Judas Agrees to Help Jesus' Enemies

The time was near for the Passover Festival. The chief priests and the religious leaders were afraid of the people. So they were trying to find a way to kill Jesus secretly. Then the Devil got into Judas Iscariot, who was one of the twelve close followers of Jesus. Judas went and told the chief priests and the officers of the Temple guard that he would be willing to hand Jesus over to them. They were pleased and offered to pay him money. Judas accepted their offer. He started looking for a time to hand Jesus over to them when the people would not know about it.

Jesus' Last Meal with His Close Followers

After sunset on the day of the Passover Festival, Jesus and his twelve close followers sat down to eat the Passover Meal. During the meal Jesus said, "I tell you, one of you will hand me over to my enemies."

Jesus' close followers were very upset, and they all began to ask him, "Surely, Lord, you don't mean me?" Jesus answered, "The one who dips his bread in the dish with me will hand me over to my enemies. God's Chosen Man will die just as our Scriptures say he will. But how terrible it will be for the man who hands him over to his enemies. That man would have been better off if he had never been born!"

Judas was the one who was going to hand Jesus over to his enemies. He spoke up and asked, "Surely, Teacher, you don't mean me?"

Jesus answered, "You are the one who said that."

While Jesus and his close followers were eating, Jesus took some bread in his hand and gave thanks to God. He broke the bread, gave it to them, and said, "Take this bread and eat it. This bread is my body."

Then Jesus took a cup of wine in his hand and gave thanks to God. He handed the cup to his close followers and said, "Take this cup and drink some of the wine. I want all of you to drink some. This wine is my blood. It will be poured out when I am put to death. This is the way God will keep his promise to forgive people's sins. Now remember. I will not drink wine again until that day I drink new wine with you in my Father's Kingdom."

After that, they all sang a hymn and went out to the Mount of Olives.

Jesus Prays in Gethsemane

After Jesus' last meal with his close followers, he went with them to a place called Gethsemane. He said to all of them except Peter and the two sons of Zebedee, "Sit down here while I go over there and pray." Then these three followers went on with Jesus. He became very sad and sorrowful. He said to the three followers, "The sorrow in my heart is so great that it is about to kill me. Wait here and stay awake while I pray."

Jesus went a little farther, threw himself face down on the ground and prayed, "My Father, please don't make me drink this cup of suffering. But if that's what you want me to do, I am willing to do it."

He went back to his three followers and found them asleep. He said to Peter, "Why can't the three of you stay awake with me for even an hour? Stay awake and pray so that you will not fail when you are put to the test. You want to do what is right, but you are weak."

Again Jesus went away and prayed, "My Father, please don't make me drink this cup of suffering. But if that is what you want me to do, I am willing to do it." When he came back, he found them asleep again. They could not keep their eyes open.

Once more Jesus left them and prayed the same prayer a third time. Then he went back to his followers and said, "Are you still resting and sleeping? Listen! The time has come for God's Chosen Man to be handed over to sinful men. Get up, let's go. Here comes the man who will hand me over to my enemies."

Jesus Before the Jewish Council

Jesus was arrested in Gethsemane and taken to the house of Caiaphas, the High Priest. The teachers of the Scriptures and other Jewish leaders had come together there. Peter followed the crowd at a distance and then went into the courtyard of the High Priest's house. He sat down there with the guards to see what was going to happen to Jesus.

The chief priests and the whole Jewish Council tried to find some people who would tell lies against Jesus, so that they could put him to death. But they could not find any reason to put Jesus to death, even though many people came and told lies about him. Finally two men stepped up and told the Council, "This man said that he could tear down God's Temple and build it back again in three days."

The High Priest stood up and asked Jesus, "What do you have to say about that?" But Jesus kept quiet. The High Priest spoke to him again and said, "I command you to tell the truth in the name of the living God. Do you claim to be God's Chosen King, the Son of God?"

Jesus answered him, "You are the one who said that. But I tell all of you that from now on you will see God's Chosen Man sitting at the right side of almighty God and coming on the clouds."

When the High Priest heard this, he tore his clothes in anger and said, "This man has spoken against God! We don't need any more witnesses. You heard how he spoke against God! What do you think?"

The men of the Council answered, "He is guilty; he must die!"

Then they spat in his face and beat him. Some of them slapped him and said, "All right, if you are God's Chosen King, try to guess who hit you!"

Jesus Before Pilate

Early in the morning Jesus was taken from Caiaphas' house to the palace of the Roman governor, but the Jewish leaders did not go inside. For according to their religion they could not eat the Passover meal if they went into a home that did not belong to a Jew. So Pilate, the governor, went outside to them. He asked, "What do you say this man has done?"

They answered, "We would not have brought him to you if he had not been guilty of a crime."

Pilate said to them, "If he has broken your Jewish law, take him and judge him yourselves."

They answered, "We do not have the power to put anyone to death on a cross." (This happened so that what Jesus had said earlier would come true, for he had said that he would be put to death on a cross.)

Pilate went back into the governor's palace and had Jesus brought in to him. He asked Jesus, "Are you the King of the Jews?"

Jesus answered, "Are you asking this question because you want to know or because other people told you about me?"

"Do you think I am a Jew?" Pilate answered. "It was your own Jewish people and the chief priests who handed you over to me. What have you done?"

Jesus said, "The Kingdom I rule is not a part of this world. If I ruled like the kings of this world, my followers would fight to keep me from being handed over to the Jewish leaders. No, my Kingdom is not like the kingdoms of this world."

So Pilate asked him, "Are you a king, then?"

Jesus answered, "You say that I am a king. I was born and came into this world for just one thing — to speak the truth about God. And whoever receives the truth listens to what I say."

"And what is that truth?" Pilate asked.

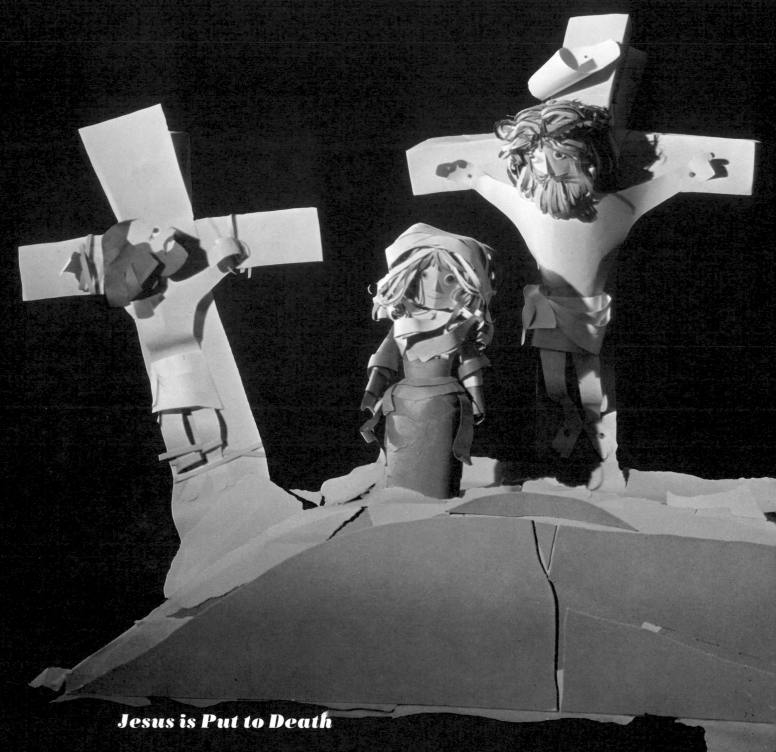

Jesus is Put to Death

Pilate handed Jesus over to the soldiers, and they led him away to be put to death. On the way they met a man from Cyrene named Simon, who was coming into the city from the country. They grabbed him and made him take the cross and carry it behind Jesus.

A large crowd of people were following Jesus. In the crowd there were some women who were crying because of what was happening to him. But Jesus turned to them and said, 'Women of Jerusalem, don't cry for me. Cry for yourselves and for your children. A time is coming when people will say, 'How lucky are the women who never had any

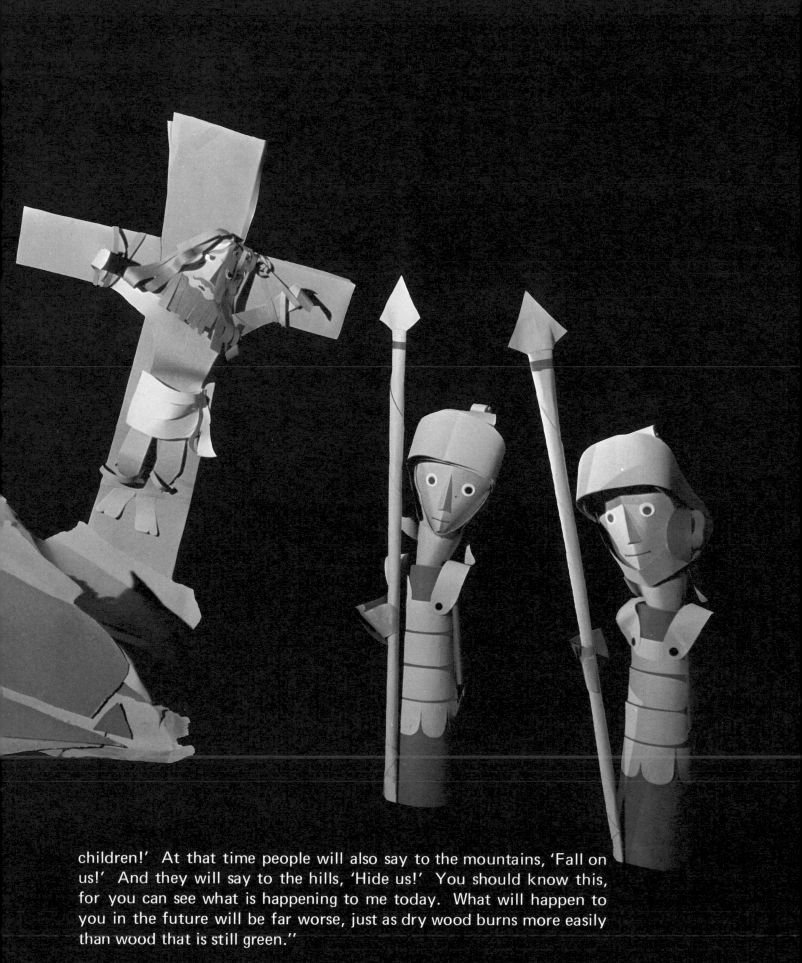

children!' At that time people will also say to the mountains, 'Fall on us!' And they will say to the hills, 'Hide us!' You should know this, for you can see what is happening to me today. What will happen to you in the future will be far worse, just as dry wood burns more easily than wood that is still green.''

Two other men, both of them criminals, were also led out to be put to death with Jesus. When they all came to the place called "The Skull", the soldiers nailed Jesus to the cross there. They also nailed each of the two criminals to a cross, one on each side of Jesus. Jesus prayed for the soldiers who had nailed him to the cross. He said, "Forgive them, Father! They don't know what they are doing."

The soldiers divided his clothing among themselves by throwing dice. The people stood there looking at Jesus, but the Jewish leaders made fun of him. They said, "He saved others from death; let him save himself if he is God's Chosen King."

The soldiers also made fun of him. They came up to him and offered him cheap wine, and said, "Save yourself if you are the King of the Jews!"

Above him were written these words: "This is the King of the Jews."

One of the criminals hanging there beside Jesus kept insulting him. He said, "Aren't you God's Chosen King? Save yourself and us!"

But the second criminal said to the one who had insulted Jesus, "Don't you fear God? You are going to die too. And we are getting what we deserve, but he has done no wrong." Then he said to Jesus, "Remember me, Jesus, when you come as King!"

Jesus said to him, "I promise you that today you will be in heaven with me."

At about twelve o'clock the sun stopped shining, and the whole country was dark until three o'clock. Then the curtain hanging in the Temple was torn in two. Jesus cried out in a loud voice, "Father, I put myself in your hands." And when he had said this, he died.

When the army officer saw what had happened, he worshipped God and said, "This must have been a good man."

When the crowds who had come there to watch saw what had happened, they beat their chests in sorrow and went back home.

94

Jesus Is Raised from Death

Early Sunday morning two women who had been followers of Jesus went to see the place where Jesus was buried. They were Mary Magdalene and the other Mary. Suddenly there was a great earthquake. An angel of the Lord came down from heaven, rolled away the stone at the opening of the tomb, and sat on it. The angel shone like a flash of lightning, and his clothes were white as snow. The guards who had been stationed at the tomb were so afraid that they trembled and fell to the ground like dead men.

Then the angel said to the two women, "Do not be afraid. I know that you are looking for Jesus, who was put to death on a cross. He is not here. God has raised him from death, just as he promised to do. Come and see the place where he was lying. Then go quickly and tell his followers that God has raised Jesus from death. Jesus is going on to Galilee ahead of them, and they can see him there. Remember what I have told you."

So the women left the tomb in a hurry. They were afraid, and yet they were very happy, as they ran to tell his followers what had happened.

Mary Magdalene Sees Jesus

Early on Sunday morning, while it was still dark, Mary Magdalene went to the tomb where Jesus was buried and saw that the stone had been taken away from the entrance. She ran to Simon Peter and to another close follower, whom Jesus loved. She said, "They have taken the Lord from the tomb, and we don't know where they have put him!"

Then Peter and the other followers went to the tomb. The two of them were running, but the other follower ran faster than Peter and reached the tomb first. He bent over and saw the linen burial cloths, but he did not go into the tomb. When Peter arrived, he went straight into the cave. He saw the burial cloths lying there and the cloth which had been tied around Jesus' head. It was not lying with the burial cloths, but was rolled up by itself. Then the other follower, who had reached the tomb first, also went in. He saw the burial cloths and believed. (They still did not understand the Scriptures which said that Jesus must rise from death.) Then the two friends of Jesus went back home.

Mary stood weeping outside the cave. While she was still weeping, she bent over and looked in. She saw two angels there. They were dressed in white and were sitting where the body of Jesus had been, one at the head and the other at the feet. They asked her, "Why are you weeping?"

She answered, "They have taken my Lord away, and I do not know where they have put him!"

Then she turned around and saw Jesus standing there, but she did not know that it was Jesus. "Why are you weeping?" Jesus asked her. "Who are you looking for?"

She thought he was the gardener, so she said to him, "If you took his body away, sir, tell me where you have put him, and I will go and get him."

Jesus said to her, "Mary!"

She turned toward him and said in the Hebrew language, "Rabboni!" (This means "Teacher".)

"Do not hold onto me," Jesus told her, "because I have not yet gone back to the Father. But go to my followers and tell them that I am returning to God. He is my Father and their Father, my God and their God."

So Mary Magdalene went and told the followers of Jesus that she had seen the Lord, and she told them what he had said.

Jesus Meets Two Followers on the Road to Emmaus

On that same day two of Jesus' followers were going from Jerusalem to a town named Emmaus, about seven miles away. They were talking to each other about all the things that had happened. As they talked and asked questions of one another, Jesus himself came and started walking along with them. When they saw him, somehow they did not know who he was. Jesus asked them, "What are you talking about with one another as you walk along?"

They stood still, with sad faces. One of them, named Cleopas, asked him, "Are you the only visitor in Jerusalem who doesn't know the things that have been happening there these last few days?"

"What things?" Jesus asked.

"The things that happened to Jesus of Nazareth, " they answered. "Jesus was a prophet, and God and all the people thought that he was powerful in everything he said and did. But our chief priests and our rulers handed him over to his enemies to be sentenced to death, and he was put to death on a cross. We were hoping that he would be the one who was going to set the people of Israel free!

"Besides all that, this is now the third day since it happened. Some of the women of our group surprised us. They went at dawn to the tomb, but could not find his body. They came back saying that they had seen a vision of angels who told them that he is alive. Then some of our group went to the tomb and found it just as the women had said, but they did not see Jesus."

Then Jesus said to them, "Why are you so foolish? Why are you so slow to believe everything the prophets said? Don't you understand that it was necessary for God's Chosen King to suffer these things? He had to suffer before he could receive the wonderful things that God had for him." Then Jesus explained to them what Moses and the prophets had written about him and what was said about him in the rest of the Scriptures.

As they came near the town of Emmaus, Jesus pretended to be going farther. But they held him back, and said, "Stay with us. The day is almost over, and it is getting dark." So he went into the house to stay with them. He sat down to eat, took the bread in his hands, and gave thanks to God for it. Then he broke the bread in pieces and gave them some. When he broke the bread, their eyes were opened, and they knew that it was Jesus. But then he disappeared, and they could not see him. They said to one another, "Wasn't it like fire burning in us when he talked to us on the road and explained the Scriptures to us?"

They got up at once and went back to Jerusalem, where they found the eleven close followers of Jesus gathered together with others who had also been his followers. The eleven told the two followers who had come from Emmaus, "The Lord has really been raised from death! He has appeared to Simon Peter!"

Then the two men from Emmaus explained what had happened on the road and how they had known that it was Jesus when he broke the bread.

Jesus' Followers Catch Fish

At Lake Galilee Jesus appeared once more to his followers. This is how it happened. Simon Peter, Thomas (called the Twin), Nathanael (the one from Cana in Galilee), the two sons of Zebedee, and two other close followers of Jesus were all together. Simon Peter said to the others, "I am going fishing."

"We will come with you," they said. So they went out onto the lake in a boat and started fishing. They fished all night and did not catch a thing. As the sun was rising, Jesus stood at the water's edge, but the men in the boat did not know that it was Jesus. Then he asked them, "Young men, haven't you caught anything?"

"Not a thing," they answered.

Jesus called to them, "Throw your net into the water on the right side of the boat, and you will catch some fish." So they threw the net out, but they could not pull it back because it was so full of fish.

The follower whom Jesus loved said to Peter, "It is the Lord!" When Peter heard that it was the Lord, he put on some clothes and jumped into the water to swim to shore. The other followers were in the boat, which was only about a hundred yards from the shore. So they came in, pulling the net full of fish. When they reached shore, they saw a charcoal fire with fish cooking on it and some bread. Then Jesus said to them, "Bring some of the fish you have just caught."

Simon Peter got back into the boat and dragged the net on shore. It was full of big fish, 153 in all. Even though there were many fish, the net did not tear. Jesus said to the men, "Come and eat." None of them dared ask him, "Who are you?" for they knew it was the Lord. Jesus went over, took the bread, and gave it to them; he did the same with the fish.

This was the third time that Jesus appeared to his followers after he was raised from death.

Thomas, the Doubting Follower of Jesus

Thomas, called the Twin, was one of the twelve close followers of Jesus. He was not with the others when Jesus appeared to them. The others told Thomas, "We have seen the Lord!"

Thomas said to them, "I will not believe unless I can see the nail holes in his hands. Before I believe, I will have to put my finger in the nail holes and my hand in the hole that the spear made in his side."

A week later Jesus' followers were gathered together again, and this time Thomas was with them. They were inside with the doors locked, but Jesus came and stood among them. He said, "Peace be with you." Then he said to Thomas, "Look at my hands and put your finger here. Reach out your hand and put it in the hole in my side. Stop your doubting and believe!"

Thomas answered him, "My Lord and my God!"

Jesus said to him, "Do you believe because you see me? How fortunate are those who believe without seeing me!"

Jesus Sends Out His Followers

The eleven close followers of Jesus went to the hill in Galilee where Jesus had told them to go. When they saw him there, they worshipped him, even though some of them doubted. Jesus came near them and said, ''God has given me all power in heaven and on earth. Go to all people everywhere and make them my followers. Baptize them in the name of the Father, the Son, and the Holy Spirit. Teach them to obey everything that I have told you to do. And I will be with you always, to the end of the world.''

Jesus Is Taken Up to Heaven

When Jesus was with his followers in Jerusalem, he said to them, "While I was still with you, I told you that all this would happen. Everything that is written about me in the Scriptures had to come true, everything that Moses and the prophets wrote and everything that is written in the Psalms."

Then he helped them understand what the Scriptures meant. He said, "It is written in the Scriptures that God's Chosen King must suffer. Then three days later he must rise from death. After that, as his messengers, you must tell the whole world about how they should turn from their sins so that God will forgive them. You must begin in Jerusalem to tell what has happened.

I will send you the Holy Spirit, which my Father has promised to give you. But you must wait here in the city of Jerusalem until this power from heaven comes down to you."

Then Jesus led his followers out of the city as far as Bethany. There he raised his hands and blessed them. As he was blessing them, he left them and was taken up into heaven. They worshipped him. Then they went back to the city with great joy and spent all their time in the Temple giving thanks to God.

The Coming of the Holy Spirit

Fifty days after the Passover Festival, on the day of Pentecost, all the followers of Jesus were gathered together in one place. Suddenly there was a noise from the sky which sounded like a strong wind. The noise filled the whole house where they were sitting. Then they saw things that looked like tongues of fire come down and touch each person there. The Holy Spirit came to all of them and they began to speak in other languages.

Religious Jews from every part of the world were living in Jerusalem. When they heard the noise, a large crowd of them gathered. They were all excited, because each one of them heard the followers of Jesus talking in his own language. In their great surprise they said to one another, "These people who are talking like this are all from Galilee! How can it be that we hear them speaking in our own native languages? We come from countries all over the world. Some of us were born Jews, and others of us have become Jews. Some of us are from Rome; some from Crete, others from Arabia, and still others from Parthia, Media, Elam, Mesopotamia, Judea, Cappadocia, Pontus, Asia, Phrygia, Pamphylia, Egypt, and the regions of Libya near Cyrene. Yet all of us hear them speaking in our own languages about the great things that God has done!" They were all amazed and confused, and they kept asking each other, "What does this mean?"

But other people made fun of Jesus' followers. They said, "These people are drunk!"

Then Peter stood up with the other eleven close followers of Jesus and began to speak to the crowd in a loud voice. He said, "Fellow Jews and all of you who live in Jerusalem, listen to me and let me tell you what this means. You think that these people are drunk. But that is not so. No one gets drunk at nine o'clock in the morning. Something else has happened. This is what God promised in the book of the prophet Joel. God said,

> "In the last days of the world
>   I will give my Spirit to everyone.
> Your sons and daughters will speak my message;
>   your young men will see visions,
>   and your old men will have dreams.
> In those days
>   I will even give my Spirit to all my servants,
>   both men and women,
>   and they will speak my message,
> And then whoever calls out to the Lord for help
>   will be saved."

"Listen, people of Israel. You had Jesus nailed to a cross, but God has made him our Lord and his Chosen King!"

When the people heard what Peter said, they were deeply troubled and said to him and to the other followers of Jesus, "What shall we do?"

Peter said, "Turn away from your sins and be baptized in the name of Jesus Christ, so that God will forgive your sins. Then you will receive God's gift of the Holy Spirit. God's promise was made to you and your children and to all the nations far away. God makes this promise to everyone he calls."

Palestine

Mediterranean Sea

Cana

GALILEE

Lake Galilee

Nazareth

SAMARIA

Jordan River

Emmaus

Jerusalem

Bethlehem

JUDEA

Dead Sea

Table of Contents

Colour separations by Lithochrome (74) Inc.

Printed by: Ashton-Potter Limited, Toronto

112